# How to use this book

*Follow the advice, in italics, given for you on each page.*
*Support the children as they read the text that is shaded in cream.*
**Praise** *the children at every step!*

*Detailed guidance is provided in the Read Write Inc. Phonics Handbook*

## 8 reading activities

*Children:*
- *Practise reading the speed sounds.*
- *Read the green and red words for the story.*
- *Listen as you read the introduction.*
- *Discuss the vocabulary check with you.*
- *Read the story.*
- *Re-read the story and discuss the 'questions to talk about'.*
- *Re-read the story with fluency and expression.*
- *Practise reading the speed words.*

# Speed sounds

## Consonants  *Say the pure sounds (do not add 'uh').*

| f ff | l ll | m mm | n nn kn | r rr | s ss | v ve | z zz s | (sh) | th | ng nk |
|---|---|---|---|---|---|---|---|---|---|---|

| b bb | c k ck | d dd | g gg | h | j | p (pp) | qu | t tt | w (wh) | x | y | ch tch |
|---|---|---|---|---|---|---|---|---|---|---|---|---|

## Vowels  *Say the sounds in and out of order.*

| at | hen head | in | on | up | day | see happy | high | blow |
|---|---|---|---|---|---|---|---|---|

| zoo | look | car | for door snore | fair | whirl | shout | boy |
|---|---|---|---|---|---|---|---|

*Each box contains one sound but sometimes more than one grapheme. Focus graphemes are **circled**.*

## Green words

*Read in Fred Talk (pure sounds).*

sp<u>oo</u>n   b<u>ow</u>l   splat

<u>g</u>oo<u>d</u>   h<u>oo</u>k   <u>sh</u><u>oo</u>k   st<u>oo</u>d   <u>wh</u><u>oo</u><u>sh</u>   w<u>oo</u>d

*Read in syllables.*

c<u>oo</u>k`b<u>oo</u>k  →  c<u>oo</u>kb<u>oo</u>k      w<u>oo</u>d`en  →  w<u>oo</u>den      past`a  →  pasta

*Read the root word first and then with the ending.*

l<u>oo</u>k  →  l<u>oo</u>king  →  l<u>oo</u>ked      c<u>oo</u>k  →  c<u>oo</u>ked

mix  →  mixed                    tip  →  ti<u>pp</u>ed

## Red words

<u>s</u><u>ai</u>d   a<u>ll</u>   he   we   my   no   so   to

5

# Vocabulary check

*Discuss the meaning (as used in the story) after the children have read each word.*

**definition:**

**stood**　　　　　　　　*put (stood a big bowl)*

*Punctuation to note in this story:*

| | |
|---|---|
| *Dad   Mum* | *Capital letters for names* |
| *Not   So   Then   Last   He* | *Capital letters that start sentences* |
| *.* | *Full stop at the end of each sentence* |
| *!* | *Exclamation mark used to show anger* |
| *...* | *Wait and see* |

# A good cook?

## Introduction

*Who does the cooking in your home?*
*What does this person like to cook best of all?*

*Dad decides to cook pasta.*
*Everything goes well until the very last moment.*

Story written by Gill Munton
Illustrated by Tim Archbold

Last Sunday, my Dad said,

"I think I'll cook pasta today."

"Good," said Mum.

"I will put my feet up."

Cooking the pasta took Dad all day!

He looked in his cookbook.

He took a pan from its hook.

He cooked the

pasta in it.

Then he shook the pan,

and mixed in cheese

with a wooden spoon.

"Mmm! Smells good!"

He stood a big bowl

on a mat.

Then he tipped up the pan ...

Whoosh! Splat!

So Mum and I cooked egg and chips!

Is my Dad a good cook?

Not yet!

# Questions to talk about

*Re-read the page. Read the question to the children. Tell them whether it is a **FIND IT** question or **PROVE IT** question.*

**FIND IT**

✓ *Turn to the page*

✓ *Read the question*

✓ *Find the answer*

**PROVE IT**

✓ *Turn to the page*

✓ *Read the question*

✓ *Find your evidence*

✓ *Explain why*

**Page 8:**   PROVE IT   *Who do you think usually does the cooking?*

**Page 9:**   PROVE IT   *Why do you think it took all day for Dad to do the cooking?*

**Page 11:**   FIND IT   *What did Dad mix into the pasta?*

**Page 12:**   PROVE IT   *How did the disaster happen?*

**Page 13:**   PROVE IT   *Do you think Mum should have cooked in the end?*